JOKE BOOK

TRY NOT TO LAUGH CHALLENGE™

10 YEAR OLD EDITION

Try Not To Laugh Challenge
BONUS PLAY

Join our Joke Club and get the Bonus Play PDF!

Simply send us an email to:

TNTLPublishing@gmail.com

and you will get the following:

- 10 Hilarious, Bonus Jokes
- An entry in our Monthly Giveaway of a $50 Amazon Gift card!

We draw a new winner each month and will contact you via email!

Good luck!

☺

WELCOME TO THE
TRY NOT TO LAUGH CHALLENGE!

RULES OF THE GAME:

★ Grab a friend or family member, a pen/pencil, and your comedic skills! Determine who will be "Jokester 1" and "Jokester 2".

★ Take turns reading the jokes aloud to each other, and check the box next to each joke you get a laugh from! Each laugh box is worth 1 point, and the pages are labeled to instruct and guide when it is each player's turn.

★ Once you have both completed telling jokes in the round, tally up your laugh points and mark it down on each score page! There is a total of 10 Rounds.

★ Play as many rounds as you like! Once you reach the last round, Round 10, tally up ALL points from the previous rounds to determine who is the CHAMPION LAUGH MASTER!

★ Round 11 - The Tie-Breaker Round.

In the event of a tie, proceed to Round 11. This round will be 'Winner Takes All!', so whoever scores more laugh points in this round alone, is crowned the CHAMPION LAUGH MASTER!

TIP: Use an expressive voice, facial expressions, and even silly body movement to really get the most out of each joke and keep the crowd laughing!

Now, it's time to play!

ROUND
1

What birthday should you celebrate by going camping?

Your TENT-h birthday!

LAUGH

The robot is acting kind of crazy today. Must have a few screws loose!

LAUGH

Why did the zombie fail the test?

He didn't have the BRAINS!

LAUGH

What's covering the ground in Miami?

Floor-duh. (Florida)

LAUGH

Why shouldn't you give baby cows soda?

☐ LAUGH

They aren't allowed to have CALF-eine!

Why should you never lie to your cat?

☐ LAUGH

They can smell a rat!

How do you speed up the moving process?

☐ LAUGH

U-Haul!

Why is it hard to drive in the African plains?

☐ LAUGH

Because there's lot's of GIRAFFE-ic! (Traffic)

Pass the book to Jokester 2! →

Who is married to Uncle Sipper?

Aunt Eater!

LAUGH

What is an owl's favorite type of clothing?

A HOO-p skirt.

LAUGH

What river makes you want to go shopping?

Amazon!

LAUGH

What did the llama say after he helped someone out?

"No prob-LLAMA!"

LAUGH

Why did the bee couple go to space?

Because it was their honeymoon!

⬜ LAUGH

Where does the letter 'X' cross the street?

In the CROSS-walk!

⬜ LAUGH

What do you call ducks on a hiking trip?

QUACK-packers!

⬜ LAUGH

What do you call a calm bison?

Buffa-LOW KEY!

⬜ LAUGH

Time to add up your points! ➡

SCORE BOARD

Add up each Jokester's laugh points
for this round!

JOKESTER 1
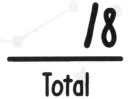
/8
Total

JOKESTER 2
/8
Total

ROUND WINNER

ROUND
2

Why and where do you keep writing utensils?

Just in case!

◻ LAUGH

Who couldn't feel their fingers when they were counting them?

NUMB-ers!

◻ LAUGH

What do you call books for kittens?

LITTER-ature!

◻ LAUGH

What subject do people like least?

SIGH-ence.

◻ LAUGH

What kind of car does a hen like to lay her eggs in?

A HATCH-back!

LAUGH ☐

Why is a gingerbread man an easy hotel guest?

He doesn't mind a CRUMBY room!

LAUGH ☐

Where do clouds stay on vacation?

AIR-bnb!

LAUGH ☐

Why did the man tell fibs when he was seaside?

He liked LYING on the beach!

LAUGH ☐

Pass the book to Jokester 2! →

What do you call a harbor that no one goes to?

A PASS-port!

LAUGH

How did the conductor get so good at his job?

Years of TRAIN-ing!

LAUGH

What kind of yogurt do pilots eat?

Plane, of course!

LAUGH

What do you win at a car-themed arcade?

Speeding tickets!

LAUGH

Why are there so many pepperonis lying around Italy?

Because they fell off of the Leaning Tower of PIZZA!

LAUGH

What is a gun's favorite basketball position?

Shooting guard!

LAUGH

What do you call a citrus medicine?

LAUGH

LEMON-aid!

Don't mess with the rope today. He is KNOT happy!

☐
LAUGH

Time to add up your points! ➡

SCORE BOARD

Add up each Jokester's laugh points for this round!

JOKESTER 1

/8

Total

JOKESTER 2

/8

Total

ROUND WINNER

ROUND 3

What's the biggest meal you can get at a hotel?

The Continental Breakfast!

LAUGH

Where do you take your car when it starts farting out?

To the nearest gas station!

LAUGH

Why are so many photographs unjustly imprisoned?

They are often FRAMED!

LAUGH

Why did the bad illustrator lose races?

He couldn't finish lines!

LAUGH

What should you use to draw a poop emoji?

A number 2 pencil!

○
LAUGH

Why didn't the baseball player ever understand what was happening?

He was always way off base!

○
LAUGH

Why was the volleyball always so paranoid?

It was worried it would be SET UP!

○
LAUGH

What do you call it when a cow remembers something new?

Deja-MOO!

○
LAUGH

Pass the book to Jokester 2! ➝

JOKESTER 2

What is an optometrist's favorite drink?

EYE-cd tea!

LAUGH

Who did the fruit call when it got injured?

The PEAR-amedic!

LAUGH

What is a dog's favorite movie?

Jurassic BARK!

LAUGH

What is the number's favorite type of car?

FOUR-d!

LAUGH

24

Why did the farmer avoid the cornfield?

○ LAUGH

He was afraid he'd get lost in the MAIZE.

What did the fly say to the spider?

"Your problem is you spend too much time on the web."

○ LAUGH

Why did the tricycle have issues?

One of the tires thought it was such a big wheel! (Big deal)

○ LAUGH

What did the cinnamon say to the dough?

"Sometimes you gotta ROLL with the punches."

○ LAUGH

Time to add up your points! →

SCORE BOARD

Add up each Jokester's laugh points for this round!

JOKESTER 1
$\dfrac{/8}{\text{Total}}$

JOKESTER 2
$\dfrac{/8}{\text{Total}}$

ROUND WINNER

ROUND

4

What do you call a bear on the beach?

A SOLAR bear!

○ LAUGH

What is a kangaroo's favorite track and field event?

The high jump!

○ LAUGH

What do you call a salamander that won't tell the truth?

An am-FIB-ian!

○ LAUGH

Why did no one like talking to the lamb?

He would always BAAA-bble on, and on, about nothing!

○ LAUGH

The tree is being mean, but I'm not worried. He's all BARK and no bite.

☐ LAUGH

What do sponges watch on TV?

Soap Operas!

☐ LAUGH

What did the train conductor say to the eagle?

"All A-BIRD!"

☐ LAUGH

How do we know that the ocean is so heavy?

☐ LAUGH

There are so many SCALES in the sea!

Pass the book to Jokester 2! →

What is a salamander's favorite snack?

Fig NEWT-ons!

○ LAUGH

Why did Dumbo lay down?

Because he was feeling ele-FAINT!

○ LAUGH

What does Bigfoot order at an Italian restaurant?

Spagh-YETI!

○ LAUGH

Why should you not let your cat control the TV remote?

They are always pressing
PAWS or MOEW-t! (Pause and Mute)

○ LAUGH

How do you tie luggage onto a spaceship?

An Astro-KNOT.

☐ LAUGH

What do you call an outfit made out of glue?

Tacky.

☐ LAUGH

I found a new dentist, but I'm too scared to tell my old dentist the TOOTH!

☐ LAUGH

What's the rapper's favorite drink?

Ice-T.

☐ LAUGH

Time to add up your points! ➡

SCORE BOARD

Add up each Jokester's laugh points for this round!

JOKESTER 1

$$\frac{}{\text{Total}}\ /8$$

JOKESTER 2

$$\frac{}{\text{Total}}\ /8$$

ROUND WINNER

ROUND

5

What kind of bird is the best writer?

A PEN-guin!

☐ LAUGH

How much space on his computer did the shark's selfie take up?

One mega-BITE!

☐ LAUGH

What animal is the star player on the nocturnal little league team?

The baseball bat!

☐ LAUGH

What is a skunk's favorite activity at school?

Show-and-SMELL!

☐ LAUGH

 **JOKESTER 1**

Why did Frankenstein go to the school nurse?

He was COFFIN!

☐ LAUGH

Is the school newspaper pretty boring?

Yeah, it's a real SNOOZE-paper.

☐ LAUGH

How do you greet your orchestra teacher?

"Cello!"

☐ LAUGH

Why is the librarian so busy?

He is always BOOK-ed.

☐ LAUGH

Pass the book to Jokester 2! →

How did the dinosaurs have such nice teeth?

○ LAUGH

They remembered to FLOSS-il twice a day!

What holds up the roof in a house made of light?

A laser beam.

○ LAUGH

Which state shares its name with an ocean of rackets and yellow balls?

Tennis-sea.

○ LAUGH

Why can't you trust a sleeping person?

They always lie!

○ LAUGH

When did the man prefer to go bowling?

In his SPARE time!

LAUGH

Why did the baseball player join the Army?

LAUGH

He wanted to be a part of the BAT-tallion!

What track event is only for girls?

The HER-dles!

LAUGH

Where did the race car go after being in an accident?

The DENT-ist!

LAUGH

Time to add up your points! ➞

SCORE BOARD

Add up each Jokester's laugh points for this round!

JOKESTER 1

<u>_____/8_____</u>
Total

JOKESTER 2

<u>_____/8_____</u>
Total

ROUND WINNER

ROUND

6

 **JOKESTER 1**

Why did the skeleton need a jacket?

He was CHILLED to the bone!

LAUGH

Where do garbage men sleep at summer camp?

On JUNK beds.

LAUGH

Did you hear about the perfume that smells like nothing?

It doesn't cost a SCENT.

LAUGH

What has two slices of bread and a membership card?

A CLUB sandwich!

LAUGH

Every fall, the trees worry that their leaves will never grow back. Every spring, when their buds finally sprout, they're re-LEAVED.

☐ LAUGH

How did the boat shop attract new customers?

Huge sails! (Sales)

☐ LAUGH

What did the trash compactor say to her first love?

This is the biggest CRUSH I've ever had.

☐ LAUGH

Why can't band-aids save up money?

They always get RIPPED off!

☐ LAUGH

Pass the book to Jokester 2! →

What did one frog say to the other, after he won the argument?

"TOAD you so!"

☐ LAUGH

What do you call an insect that doesn't brag?

A HUMBLE-bee!

☐ LAUGH

Why wouldn't the bald porcupine stand up for itself?

It was spineless!

☐ LAUGH

What do you call it when a lion works on your car?

MANE-tenance.

☐ LAUGH

42

JOKESTER 2

What do you do if you can't see your iPhone?

Get an EYE-pad!

☐ LAUGH

How did the boats crash at the same time?

They were in sink! (In sync)

☐ LAUGH

Why did the phone's business come to a stop?

They didn't CHARGE enough!

☐ LAUGH

Why do people like mystery jokes so much?

They're so PUN-predictable.

☐ LAUGH

Time to add up your points! →

43

SCORE BOARD

Add up each Jokester's laugh points for this round!

JOKESTER 1

/8

Total

JOKESTER 2

/8

Total

ROUND WINNER

ROUND 7

Why is the music teacher mad at the dance team?

The dance team broke a RECORD.

◯ LAUGH

The maid was full of secrets, but for the most part, she swept them under the rug.

◯ LAUGH

What do you call a library book you read on the toilet?

Over-DOO!

◯ LAUGH

No one liked sharing their ideas with the tiger. He tends to be a copy cat!

◯ LAUGH

What clothes does a dog wear when it's hot out?

Pants!

LAUGH

Why do oceanography students get bad grades?

They only strive for seas! (C's)

LAUGH

What do you call it when a chicken gives you advice?

A fowl tip!

LAUGH

Why did the long hair have road rage?

Someone cut it off!

LAUGH

Pass the book to Jokester 2! →

Why does Mississippi have the best sight?

It has the most eyes! (I's)

☐ LAUGH

What is a cows favorite game?

Truth or DAIRY!

☐ LAUGH

How do bees talk to each other?

They use buzz words.

☐ LAUGH

Why did the bird fly into the tree branch?

Just BEAK-cause!

☐ LAUGH

 **JOKESTER 2**

What do rude boats do?

They BARGE in.

☐ LAUGH

Why did the bucket get sunburned?

It was pale!

☐ LAUGH

What makes a pencil even smarter?

A sharpener!

☐ LAUGH

What kind of notebook keeps going around in circles?

Spiral!

☐ LAUGH

Time to add up your points! →

SCORE BOARD

Add up each Jokester's laugh points for this round!

JOKESTER 1 $\dfrac{\quad\quad}{\text{Total}}$ /8

JOKESTER 2 $\dfrac{\quad\quad}{\text{Total}}$ /8

$$\overline{\hspace{4cm}}$$
ROUND WINNER

ROUND

8

Have you seen the new eel documentary?

It's very SHOCK-ing!

LAUGH

What do ghouls send from vacation?

GHOST-cards!

LAUGH

What do you call an alien grandma's sweets?

Moon Pies!

LAUGH

What sport do people play on the beach?

BAY-sball!

LAUGH

JOKESTER 1

Do addition and multiplication problems get along?

SUM times.

☐ LAUGH

What should you wear to a fireman's wedding?

A soot.

☐ LAUGH

When my coat is bad, I hang it up. When it's good, I let it off the hook.

☐ LAUGH

Why did the cowboy have sore legs?

☐ LAUGH

He spent a lot of time training his CALVES.

Pass the book to Jokester 2! →

Why did the two bulls avoid each other?

They've got BEEF with each other!

☐ LAUGH

What's a Smurf's favorite type of music?

The Blues!

☐ LAUGH

What day do 1 + 1 get together?

TWOS-day.

☐ LAUGH

Why couldn't the unicorn wear her new hoodie to school?

☐ LAUGH

It wasn't part of the school UNI-form.

JOKESTER 2

Where is the lion's barbershop located?

MANE Street.

⬜ LAUGH

Why did the tree think it was a dog?

It had BARK!

⬜ LAUGH

How did the genius win the race?

Well, he got a BIG HEAD start!

⬜ LAUGH

Who is famous for making fuzzy clay pieces?

Harry Potter!

⬜ LAUGH

Time to add up your points! →

SCORE BOARD

Add up each Jokester's laugh points
for this round!

JOKESTER 1

$$\frac{/8}{\text{Total}}$$

JOKESTER 2

$$\frac{/8}{\text{Total}}$$

ROUND WINNER

ROUND

9

What metal do thieves love?

Steel.

LAUGH

What piece of clothing scares away animals?

Shoo!

LAUGH

Which country tastes best with crackers?

Chile!

LAUGH

What kind of trip does the letter 'O' take?

A ROUND trip!

LAUGH

 **JOKESTER 1**

Why is it easy to argue with a left-handed person?

Because they're never RIGHT!

☐ LAUGH

How do you know when someone who sews clothes is worn out?

Because they seamstressed!

☐ LAUGH

What do you call someone who puts themself in the middle of a room?

Self-centered!

☐ LAUGH

What do you call a ferret with a truck?

A diesel weasel!

☐ LAUGH

Pass the book to Jokester 2! →

What do you call a polar bear that's all by himself?

ICE-olated!

LAUGH

How did the golfers know they'd be friends when they were about to hit the ball?

Because they hit it off!

LAUGH

Why did the rocket leave Earth?

There wasn't enough SPACE on the ground.

LAUGH

What do you call a crustacean who works for the Mafia?

A lobster mobster!

LAUGH

The waterfall had a bad date last night. I guess he MIST his chance!

☐ LAUGH

Why did the driver paint a four leaf clover on his semi?

For good TRUCK!

☐ LAUGH

What a turkey's favorite Halloween costume?

A GOBBLE-in!

☐ LAUGH

Do you know about the least interesting pig in the world?

He's such a BOAR.

☐ LAUGH

Time to add up your points! →

SCORE BOARD

Add up each Jokester's laugh points
for this round!

JOKESTER 1 $\dfrac{\hspace{3em}}{\text{Total}}\ /8$

JOKESTER 2 $\dfrac{\hspace{3em}}{\text{Total}}\ /8$

ROUND WINNER

ROUND
10

What's the corniest breed of dog?
The HUSK-y!

LAUGH

What kind of vegetable loves to take selfies?
Snap peas!

LAUGH

What kind of make-up do lady ghosts wear?
Mas-SCARE-ya!

LAUGH

Why don't band-aids have serious arguments?
They're good at patching things up!

LAUGH

 **JOKESTER 1**

Why was the car a good archer?

It was very ACURA-te!

LAUGH

What is a zombie's favorite thing to do in the swimming pool?

Go off the DIE-ving board!

LAUGH

What kind of homework tastes good?

Assign-MINTS!

LAUGH

What subject will send you to the nurse's office?

Mu-SICK!

LAUGH

Pass the book to Jokester 2! →

Why did the wad of bubblegum extend his vacation?

He wanted to STICK around!

LAUGH

What has two wheels and sits at an angle?

Half a car!

LAUGH

Why did the locksmith go to Florida?

LAUGH

He wanted to work on the Florida Keys!

Why did the farmer's family have only one train ticket?

His cows had the UDDERS!

LAUGH

What did the dentist say when he went to court?

"The tooth, the whole tooth, and nothing but the tooth."

☐ LAUGH

Why did the mouse tell on her little brother?

To RAT him out!

☐ LAUGH

Where do thunderstorms keep their photos?

In the CLOUD!

☐ LAUGH

I got this venison for super cheap!
It was only a BUCK per pound.

☐ LAUGH

Time to add up your points! →

SCORE BOARD

Add up each Jokester's laugh points
for this round!

JOKESTER 1

$\dfrac{}{\text{Total}}$ /8

JOKESTER 2

$\dfrac{}{\text{Total}}$ /8

ROUND WINNER

Add up all your points from each round.
The Jokester with the most points is crowned

The Laugh Master!

In the event of a tie, continue to Round 11
- The Tie-Breaker Round!

JOKESTER 1 _____
Grand Total

JOKESTER 2 _____
Grand Total

THE LAUGH MASTER

ROUND

11

TIE-BREAKER
(Winner Takes ALL!)

What is silverware's favorite sports team?

The Chicago Bowls!

○ LAUGH

What is a cow's favorite play in baseball?

The dou-BULL play!

○ LAUGH

What do lumberjacks order in a Chinese restaurant?

CHOP Suey!

○ LAUGH

Why did the girl give the jeweler her phone number?

She hoped he would give her a RING!

○ LAUGH

 **JOKESTER 1**

Which state always knows what's going on?

Del-AWARE!

LAUGH

What's the difference between math and good toilet paper?

One multiplies, the other's multi-ply.

LAUGH

What gets bigger every time you share it with someone?

A lie!

LAUGH

How can you tell if a bakery is good?

If they make a lot of dough!

LAUGH

Pass the book to Jokester 2! →

Why didn't the fruit go to jail?

The Constitution protects
'Freedom of Peach'.

LAUGH

What happened when the otters started to drift apart?

They decided they wanted to see
OTTER people!

LAUGH

What do you call a sad king?

SIGH-er.

LAUGH

What's the difference between a penguin and a reindeer?

Lots of things: they're POLAR opposites!

LAUGH

 **JOKESTER 2**

What did 5 say, when the waiter asked "Party of 2?"
"Yes, just 4 1."

◻ LAUGH

Why did the butcher ask the sausage for advice?
He wanted a FRANK opinion!

◻ LAUGH

Why are most jets gray?
They like to keep their look PLANE.

◻ LAUGH

What's the difference between surfing in Hawaii and surfing the web?
On one you see all the sights, and the other you see all the sites!

◻ LAUGH

Time to add up your points! →

Add up all your points from the
Tie-Breaker Round.
The Jokester with the most points is crowned

The Laugh Master!

JOKESTER 1   /8
                    ‾‾‾‾‾‾‾
                    Total

JOKESTER 2   /8
                    ‾‾‾‾‾‾‾
                    Total

THE LAUGH MASTER

Check out our

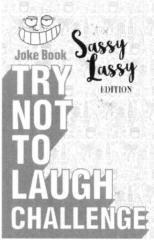

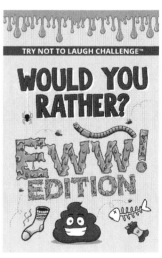

Visit our Amazon Store at:

other joke books!

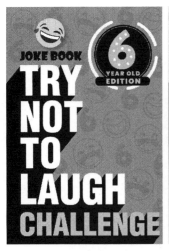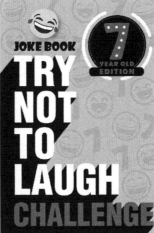

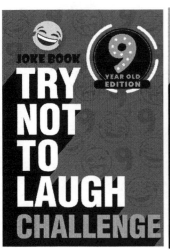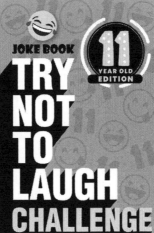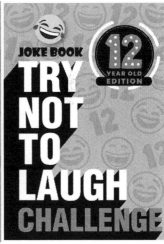

Made in the USA
Middletown, DE
13 November 2020

23881277R00046